SUNDAY EXPRESS & DAILY EXPRESS
CARTOONS

Twenty-seventh Series

A DAILY EXPRESS PUBLICATION

© 1973 Beaverbrook Newspapers Limited, Fleet Street, London, E.C.4.
CANADA: The COPP CLARK Publishing Company 517 Wellington Street West, Toronto 2B

INTRODUCTION

by

MICHAEL
PARKINSON

To say that Carl Giles is a good cartoonist is like saying George Gershwin wrote some nice tunes or Garfield Sobers is a lovely cricketer. It misses the fundamental point of the man: that he is a genius. He will blush at the word but I use it unhesitatingly. I did not even have to think twice about it.

A catalogue of Giles cartoons is a history of our time revealing not simply the mood of the moment but also charting our changing environment. Looking beyond his foreground characters and in the background, you see a church drawn with loving reverence, a street full of important detail, a tree depicting the season. These backgrounds are important because they hold a clue to the artist's love of the land we live in. It is this love of his subject matter that permeates his work. I am not suggesting that Giles is a soppy romantic. Far from it. But the real quality of his work that I find most appealing is his gentle, quizzical, slightly mocking love of the lot of us, warts and all.

His humour is never hurtful or vicious. It touches all of us who are possessed of that most important human quality, the ability to laugh at ourselves. The man who can make us do that is not simply a gifted cartoonist, he is an important part of our lives and therefore he is blessed.

Michael Parkinson

"Bad enough them holding their Olympics same time as us."

Sunday Express, September 10th, 1972

"Next time they offer you a golden handshake I'll settle for the clock."

(*News headline: "Presented with Donkey for Retirement Gift."*)

Daily Express, September 12th, 1972

"If you will run on about how many Messerschmitts you shot down during the Battle of Britain in front of our German au pair girl . . ."

"Grandma, it's not fair to send Vera all that way on her own to open your letters."

Daily Express, September 22nd, 1972

"Psst! On with your fig leaves!"

Sunday Express, September 24th, 1972

"Gentleman says he got hold of three nice pieces of skate. He'd like two well done and young Archie would like his medium."

Daily Express, September 28th, 1972

"I would remind you that All Good Gifts Around Us have been carefully checked before the sermon."

Sunday Express, October 1st, 1972

"It all started when he swopped 'Watchdog' for 'interfering old lady dog'."

Daily Express, October 3rd, 1972

"Anyone who has had as much to do with horses as yer actual Queen Mother will understand most of the words in your script, Mr. Garnett."

Daily Express, October 5th, 1972

"Well, it certainly isn't Barbara Castle."

(News item: "Girl's picture always by P.M.'s bed.")

Daily Express, October 10th, 1972

"You're not playing football till Saturday, anyway."

Daily Express, October 12th, 1972

"Other bar, everybody—if you don't want to get caught for a Grandma's Day session."

Sunday Express, October 15th, 1972

"I didn't see much I liked in the way of cars . . ."

Daily Express, October 17th, 1972

"This is your new nurse—Henrietta. She lied about her age to serve her country, she's only twelve."

Daily Express, October 19th, 1972

"BBC? I'd like an action replay when my husband comes home—I've just
seen him in the second row Block B working late at the office."

Sunday Express, October 22nd, 1972

"If they're going to start meeting violence with violence . . ."

Daily Express, October 24th, 1972

"If HRH puts her horse down in that puddle once more, HRH is going to lose quite a lot of my goodwill."

Sunday Express, October 29th, 1972

"All right! Don't push!"

Daily Express, October 31st, 1972

"Your 15 per cent pay rise don't make you Chief Constable, Bert Jenkins."

Daily Express, November 2nd, 1972

"As he's making us have our fireworks in the daylight because he wants to watch the
Royal Variety Show I hope nothing happens to his TV aerial."

Sunday Express, November 5th, 1972

"Why did he put us out on the roof? Because he caught sight of your book about slap-happy porters and insolent hotel staff, for one reason."

Daily Express, November 7th, 1972

"I can see 'em now—'Oo! A little silver gravy boat, just what we wanted'."

Daily Express, November 9th, 1972

"I see they're putting on a Party Political Broadcast instead of Macbeth on Christmas night, and running Macbeth instead of Football on Boxing Day."

Sunday Express, November 12th, 1972

"She'll give you 'Sportsman of the Year' if you miss."

Daily Express, November 14th, 1972

"Not only the Catering Department of the Senior Service who are on the fiddle, eh, Admiral?"

Daily Express, November 16th, 1972

"Daddy would be much happier if you didn't keep referring to 25 years ago as 'Medieval Times'."

Sunday Express, November 19th, 1972

"We don't have problems with 150 m.p.h. supertrains on our line, do we, Harry?"

Daily Express, November 21st, 1972

"Mother! Gentleman from the Polls wants your opinion on Fox Hunting."

Sunday Express, November 26th, 1972

"Now see here, Dr. Thomas, we know all about the B.M.A. survey on the shortage of accommodation for hospital doctors . . ."

Daily Express, November 28th, 1972

"Right! Let the sex maniacs in."

Daily Express, November 30th, 1972

"Do you think I would leave you walking . . . When there's room on my horse for two . . . ♪"

(P.M. had announced that something would have to be done about traffic in Downing Street and Westminster.)

Sunday Express, December 3rd, 1972

"You say this is the first time in a pub, young fella? Then I'd hop out of wee Jock's chair or it could be your last."

Daily Express, December 5th, 1972

"Relax! We haven't got to emigrate to the States after all. Tom and Jerry have got a reprieve."

Daily Express, December 8th, 1972

"Good morning, Doctor—I work in Harridge's Merry Gifts Department. I'd like a broken arm for the next two weeks."

Daily Express, December 12th, 1972

"I don't think our Captain will doze off—I've just slipped a couple of my Laxitivo Pills in his tea."

Daily Express, December 14th, 1972

"It's the garage, Dad—the 'Happy Motorist Car Washer' you've bought Mum for Christmas is in."

Daily Express, December 19th, 1972

"I've just had a happy Christmas thought—I forgot to get Auntie Vi's present."

Daily Express, December 23rd, 1972

"Bert! We've got three wise men calling for their turkeys."

Sunday Express, December 24th, 1972

"The purpose of this sale is to dispose of our own surplus junk, madam, not to acquire yours."

Daily Express, December 28th, 1972

"5 . . . 4 . . . 3 . . . 2 . . . 1 . . . Zero!! *POP!!* we're in!"

Sunday Express, December 31st, 1972

"Never mind about one big European family—I'm not calling Mrs. Smith 'Au-pair' and he's going to stop kissing me on both cheeks."

Daily Express, January 2nd, 1973

"Obviously a sailing type himself—the way he told us to push off."

"Marked increase in violence—thanks to their adoption of ideas European and beef £1 a pound."

Sunday Express, January 7th, 1973

"A plague on the high price of beef, that's what I say."

Daily Express, January 9th, 1973

"Like with P & O, there are going to be some complaints from half the passengers on this cruise when we get home."

Daily Express, January 11th, 1973

"Cancel your yacht and the holiday in Sunny Seychelles, Mother—I don't think he's sold 'em."

Sunday Express, January 14th, 1973

"I hope you put the children to bed before that Warhol sex film came on."

Daily Express, January 16th, 1973

"Yes, I did hear how the lady in Mr. Warhol's film did her painting, but we in Class 2 are sticking to the old-fashioned brush method."

Daily Express, January 18th, 1973

"I know I should be grateful in my nice warm bed, but I bet the poor harassed cod men don't have the damn stuff steamed day in day out."

Sunday Express, January 21st, 1973

"You should be able to get some good pictures of Lieut. Phillips. If you read the small print you'll find you've just signed on for 10 years in the Dragoons."

Daily Express, January 23rd, 1973

"I suppose taking the seats out so they can't cut them up is one way of preventing vandalism."

Daily Express, January 25th, 1973

"If you don't want to be a redundant Assistant Manager, remember his bad week in the City and miss it."

Sunday Express, January 28th, 1973

"Right—let's get your check-up over before the Porn-Squads swoop."

Daily Express, January 30th, 1973

"Richard, you must have a word with the newsagent about these holes in the paper."

Daily Express, February 1st, 1973

"There's certainly no discrimination between the sexes in this house. I let the women graduate from menial kitchen duties to concrete mixing and so forth."

Sunday Express, February 4th, 1973

"We, the Local Council, consider your application to build a kennel for your Fido would constitute a violation of the rural charms of the area."

Daily Express, February 6th, 1973

"Actually Charlie has read the notice, but that lamp he picked up was a trifle warm."

Daily Express, February 8th, 1973

"This lady claims that your dog has just devalued her Cruft's champ."

Sunday Express, February 11th, 1973

"Mr. Stevens felt chilly—his gas fire went out."

Daily Express, February 15th, 1973

"A word before you go, Mr. Thomas—about the coach trip I hear you're organising to see this Last Tango."

Sunday Express, February 18th, 1973

"And get him out of the window for a start."

Daily Express, February 20th, 1973

"Relax, Miss Whitebait—he's only taking his hat off."

Daily Express, February 22nd, 1973

"May I mention, with the greatest respect, Madam, that you have just knocked my Sergeant base over tip."

Sunday Express, February 25th, 1973

"I see they did not think much of your offer to take their minds off the national crisis by doing your bird and animal imitations."

Daily Express, February 27th, 1973

"What do you mean you couldn't get to work because of the rail strike? You only live over there!"

Daily Express, March 1st, 1973

"Right! 8p a head. Who's going to be Chancellor?"

Daily Express, March 6th, 1973

"You say you're running a Get-you-to-work service from South London to Westminster? Who's your navigator?"

Daily Express, March 9th, 1973

"Come rail strikes, hell and high water—nothing will stop your Aunt Millie getting here for lunch on Sunday."

Sunday Express, March 11th, 1973

"In the meantime I'm prepared to put up with me sunken bath. Boy, another bucket of asses' milk."

Daily Express, March 13th, 1973

"You haven't been delayed getting home from the office. You've been to see 'Last Tango'."

Daily Express March 15th, 1973

"As some of us never touch a drop there must be some of us getting a double ration."

Daily Express, March 20th, 1973

"If thou paid six camels for that blue-eyed fair-skinned maiden thou paid dear."
(*News item: "Arabs offer to buy schoolgirls on holiday."*)

Daily Express, March 22nd, 1973

"We packed the children off to the Safari Park for a bit of peace."

Sunday Express, March 25th, 1973

"We know—you'd have to pay VAT if you bought one after Saturday."

Daily Express, March 27th, 1973

"The house is on fire and I've broken my leg apprehending a burglar—ask your Dad if it's all right for me to dial 999."

Daily Express, March 29th. 1973

"Mummy says as you forgot to take her breakfast up for Mother's Day she forgot to get up and get your lunch."

Sunday Express, April 1st, 1973

"I know I haven't got the hang of it yet—she's just charged me VAT."

Daily Express, April 3rd, 1973

"I know it's a good catch—but you can't fry ruddy rifles."

(News headline: "Boatload of Smuggled Arms were Dumped in the Irish Sea.")

Daily Express, April 5th, 1973

"YOU told them all to be up early if they wanted to go to Silverstone."

Daily Express, April 7th, 1973

"If we skip the reception and you step on it, we can just make Silverstone in time for the International Trophy."

Sunday Express, April 8th, 1973

"The Board appreciates you have a few shares in the Disney Empire but does not appreciate your three hour lunch to celebrate Mickey Mouse's fiftieth birthday."

Daily Express, April 10th, 1973

"Remember who I told you to vote for, Spencer—and don't you let them change your mind between here and the polls."

Daily Express. April 12th. 1973

"I'd skip it today, luv—his Lordship's not very happy about the Russians stuffing his butter at 8p a lb."

Sunday Express, April 15th, 1973

"For heaven's sake, Ruth—you don't have to frisk the boy every time he brings you a goddamn Martini."

Daily Express, April 17th, 1973

"Brace yourself, Sir, here she comes."

Daily Express, April 19th, 1973

"I knew that registrar would bungle two dozen Easter weddings at the same time—here comes *your* bridegroom now."

Sunday Express, April 22nd, 1973

"Your wife nailing you and your boat up for Easter is hardly a case for calling out the RNLI."

Daily Express, April 24th, 1973

"That's right—you DID hear me tell them to go and get lost for four days up a mountain."

Daily Express, April 26th, 1973

"I like this bit—where she stopped singing in the bath when she caught sight of our microphone."

Sunday Express, April 29th, 1973

"No, Father Bear WOULDN'T have found out quicker who'd been eating his porridge if he'd had the joint bugged!"

Daily Express, May 3rd, 1973

"Thank little Olga for taking their minds off football."

Sunday Express, May 6th, 1973

"We are the B.R.S. Lost Property Department, old boy. I believe somebody left a lorry load of tigers somewhere around here."

(News headline: "Tigers Parked all Night in London Suburb.")

Daily Express, May 8th, 1973

"All right, nurse, you've had your little joke—now get down and take that off the board."

Daily Express, May 10th, 1973

"You read that the secretarial agencies are calling for grannies and older
women? Well, your wife has engaged one for you in my place."

Daily Express, May 15th, 1973

"Mrs. Hicks, I have been in the Force around here for thirty-five years and this is no time for you to be asking me if I am wearing a real uniform."

Daily Express, May 17th, 1973

"Genuine Top of the Pops or not—thirty-three times without a break is enough."

Sunday Express, May 20th, 1973

"Signal from H.M.S. Jupiter, Sir. 'Landed 10 lb. Icelandic cod. Frying tonight'."

Daily Express, May 22nd, 1973

"If YOUR conscience is absolutely clear why are you pouring your coffee in your egg?"

Daily Express, May 24th, 1973

"'Ere, YOU!"

Sunday Express, May 27th, 1973

"It's her 'My father's got more call girls than yours' attitude that turns me off."

Daily Express, May 29th, 1973

"They are not compulsory for all of us—only for those among us with motor cycles."

"I know who else should be getting a bonus from Boots."

Daily Express, June 5th, 1973

"Well, it's one way of making 'em stop."

(News item: "Mayor accidentally hits bus with arrow.")

Daily Express, June 12th, 1973

"I'm certainly a rat in London's treadmill until Harry Hyams lets this lot and gets the bleeding lifts working."

Daily Express, June 14th, 1973

"You may remember you bought me a spare tyre for the car on Mother's Day."

Sunday Express, June 17th, 1973

"I don't think we'll have much trouble from a certain lady journalist 'reporting the fashion scene'."

Daily Express, June 19th, 1973

"I simply remarked, mother, that after today the nights start drawing in."

Daily Express, June 21st, 1973

"All those in favour of the Wimbledon strike spreading to Arcadia Tennis Club say 'Aye'."

Sunday Express, June 24th, 1973

"I'll say he was brave to keep smiling all through Mr. Brezhnev's visit—that first hug by Honeybear cracked four of his ribs."

Daily Express, June 26th, 1973

"Mum told me to give you a standing ovation for boiling your own egg."

Daily Express, June 28th, 1973

"Martha! Come back at once!"

Sunday Express, July 1st, 1973

"Whoops! There go your chances of being selected for the Admiral's Cup."

Daily Express, July 3rd, 1973

"It is no use, Tom—she says there will be only one Bjorn Borg."

Daily Express, July 5th, 1973

"'Ow you say in Anglais—'Ard up but 'appy, yes?"

Sunday Express, July 8th, 1973

"Right—I'll explain 'Payola'. I want to get my latest play on TV and you're a call girl."

Daily Express, July 12th, 1973

"Pity, now we'll have to think of something else for your brother's wedding present."

Daily Express, July 14th, 1973

"Now be a good doggie and tell the gentleman if you've eaten his ball."

Sunday Express, July 15th, 1973

"On behalf of all your teachers, Ronald, I cannot express too deeply our sorrow that end of term brings us to the parting of the ways."

Daily Express, July 19th, 1973

"Right. Let's start with 'Failure to wear a crash helmet'."

Sunday Express, August 19th, 1973

"I charge Vera danger money for collecting her aspirins."

Daily Express, August 29th, 1973

"Not perhaps a bomb, but a fairly large firework, maybe."

(The Piano Publicity Association are launching a scheme to give the piano a new "fun" image)

Sunday Express, August 26th, 1973

"He wasn't exactly shop-lifting, Madam, we caught him trying to re-plant the new school suit you bought him."

Daily Express, August 30th, 1973

"Permission to speak, Sir? In view of the sudden rise in the cost of living I would like to apply for a pay increase."

Daily Express, September 6th, 1973

"I suppose some of us are already thinking of £468,000,000 in terms of lunchtime trips to the Folies Bergere and back."

Daily Express, September 13th, 1973

"I have heard that you do not believe there is a shortage of teachers, and that in your opinion there is, in fact, one too many in this class."

Daily Express, September 20th, 1973

Printed in Great Britain by Purnell and Sons, Ltd., Paulton (Somerset) and London